Dr. Brown Present's

It's Time to Pack!

Written by
Dr. Tiffany Q. Brown
Caleb D. Brown

Illustrated by
Khadija Maryam

This book was created to help children with speech delays build on their language skills and expand their vocabulary. Co-Author Caleb D. Brown is a speech delayed child with autism and reading repetitive books has helped increase his vocabulary.

Thank you to our family and friends who have been supportive of this book. Also, special thanks to Malica Dunnock and Chauntelle Akinnuoye for their assistance.

Dedication

This book is dedicated to Dr. Brown's mother, Ernestine Johnson and her grandmother, Shirley Johnson.

It's time to pack! What do I need?

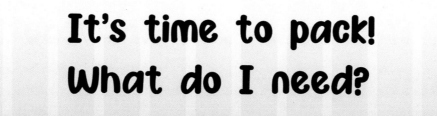

I need a toothbrush and toothpaste to brush my teeth.

It's time to pack!
What do I need?

I need clothes and underwear to cover my body.

It's time to pack!
What do I need?

I need soap so I can stay clean.

It's time to pack!
What do I need?

I need shoes to cover my feet.

It's time to pack!
What do I need?

I need pajamas to go to sleep.

It's time to pack!
What do I need?

I need swimwear for the beach.

It's time to pack!
What do I need?

I need water goggles so that
I can see the sea.

It's time to pack!
What do I need?

I need my favorite toys just for me!

It's time to pack!
What do I need?

I need my floppy hat and sunshades to look cool in the pool.

It's time to pack!
What do I need?

I need my lab jacket and stethoscope just in case...

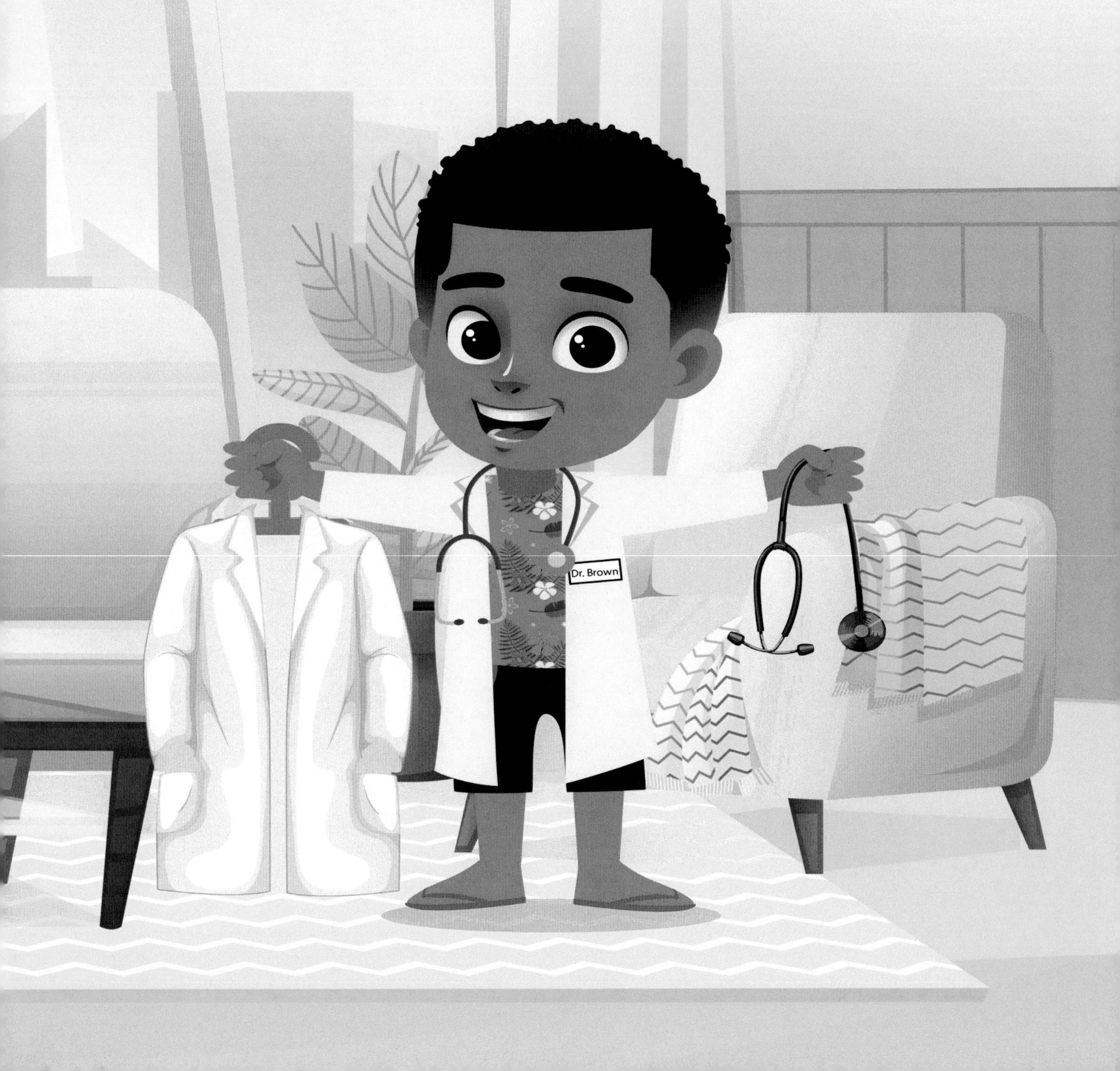

It's time to pack!
What do I need?

I need basic essentials to protect me from germs.

It's time to pack! What do I need?

I need luggage to hold my things.

I'm all packed! Now what do I do?

Time to head to the airport with my crew.

THE END

Thank you
Dr. Tiffany Brown

Made in the USA
Monee, IL
25 October 2021